Snacking

 Brushing

 Dressing

 Reading

Our Bedtime Tour

 Taping

 Waiting

 Goofing

 Fishing

 Ant

 Boating

Duck

10 Minutes till Bedtime

PEGGY RATHMANN

SCHOLASTIC INC.
New York Toronto London Auckland Sydney
Mexico City New Delhi Hong Kong

ISBN 0-439-13228-2

12 11 10 9 8 7 6 5 4 3 2 1   9/9 0 1 2 3 4/0

Printed in Mexico   49

First Scholastic printing, September 1999

Lettering by David Gatti

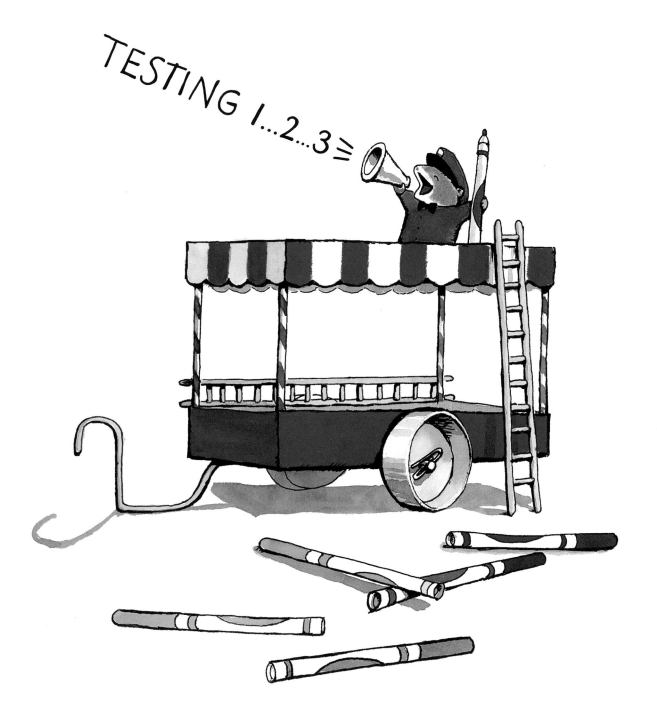

WELCOME